Helping o

This book belongs to

_____

Written by Stephen Barnett
Illustrated by Rosie Brooks

Contents

About this book

Through simple sentences, this book helps young learners learn about the value of helping everybody around them. The section on new words enhances their vocabulary too.

Helping others

It is good to be helpful.

This is the street where I live.

This is my
home.

This is my mother and my father.

This is my family.

My mother helps me to make things.

Me and my father are playing a game.

My brother is taller than me.

He helps me to climb trees.

Sometimes I help others.

I help kittens.

I help my grandmother.

I help little birds too.

We all help
each other.

New words

bird

brother

climb

each

father

games

good

grandmother

help

helpful

home

kitten

little

live

make

mother

other

others

play

sometimes

street

things

trees

What did you learn?

How many people are there in the girl's family?

What does the mother help the girl to do?

What does the father help the girl with?

Is the girl's brother taller or shorter than her?